Zaner-Bloser
Handwriting

zoom

ZB Zaner-Bloser

Credits

Art: John Hovell: 33–35, 151

Photos: ©Getty Images: Cover; ©Creatas/Getty: TOC (top); ©iStockphoto.com/Claudiad: TOC (bottom); George C. Anderson Photography, Inc.: 5, 6, 26–30; ©Westend61 GmbH/Alamy: 8 (left); ©iStockphoto.com/mcpix: 8 (right); ©iStockphoto.com/maciul7: 9 (left); ©iStockphoto.com/jcyoung2: 9 (right); ©Katrina Brown/Alamy: 10; Zaner-Bloser: 11 (left), 66, 141; ©Photosindia/Getty Images: 11 (right); ©Design Pics Inc./Alamy: 12; ©RayArt Graphics/Alamy: 13; ©iStockphoto.com/compassandcamera: 14; ©JUPITERIMAGES/Brand X/Alamy: 15 (left); ©iStockphoto.com/bmcentl: 15 (right); ©scenicireland.com/Christopher Hill Photographic/Alamy: 16 (left); ©Cultura/Alamy: 16 (top right); ©Ariel Skelley/CORBIS: 18 (bottom right); ©Ian Shaw/Alamy: 17 (left); ©Bruce Laurance/Photolibrary: 17 (right); ©Digital Vision/Getty Images: 18–19; ©Akihiro Sugimoto/Photolibrary: 20–21; ©Kevin Schafer/Corbis: 22–23; ©Visions of America, LLC/Alamy: 23 (bottom); ©iStockphoto.com/Floortje: 25 (left); ©Comstock/Jupiterimages: 25 (right); ©Creatas/Getty: 39; ©iStockphoto.com/tulcarion: 40; ©Medioimages/Photodisc/Getty Images: 41; ©iStockphoto.com/sydem: 42; ©iStockphoto.com/Claudiad: 43; ©iStockphoto.com/billnoll: 44; ©Brand X Pictures/Jupiterimages: 45; ©iStockphoto.com/jeannehatch: 46; ©iStockphoto.com/ladyminnie: 47; ©Carey Alan & Sandy/Photolibrary: 48; ©iStockphoto.com/Freder: 49; ©iStockphoto.com/Adventure_Photo: 50; ©iStockphoto.com/cinoby: 51; ©iStockphoto.com/matka_Wariatka: 52; ©iStockphoto.com/Andrea_Hill: 53; ©Matt Oldfield/Getty Images: 54; ©iStockphoto.com/Malven: 55; ©Ryan McGinnis/Alamy: 57; ©Neo Vision/Getty Images: 68; ©Alan SCHEIN/Alamy: 61; ©iStockphoto.com/stevenallan: 62; ©LWA-Sharie Kennedy/Corbis: 63; ©Brand X Pictures/Getty Images: 64; ©iStockphoto.com/alexxxl1981: 65; ©Stephen Marks/Getty Images: 67; ©Big Cheese Photo/Jupiterimages: 68; ©Brand X Pictures/Jupiterimages: 69; ©iStockphoto.com/DarrenFisher: 70;

©Wes Thompson/CORBIS: 72; ©Digital Vision/Getty Images: 73; ©iStockphoto.com/iPandastudio: 74; ©age fotostock/SuperStock: 75; ©iStockphoto.com/JulienGrondin: 76; ©iStockphoto.com/SkyF: 77; ©ilian studio/Alamy: 78; ©Li Ding/Alamy: 79; ©PhotosIndia.com/Getty Images: 80; ©iStockphoto.com/mjbs: 84; ©ImagesBazaar/Alamy: 87; ©imagebroker/Alamy: 88; ©iStockphoto.com/gmnicholas: 89; ©Brandon Seidel/Alamy: 93; ©iStockphoto.com/digitalskillet: 94; ©iStockphoto.com/ManoAfrica: 95; ©Brand X/Corbis: 96; ©Jim Batty/Alamy: 97; ©Tom Schierlitz/Getty Images 98 (left); ©Martin Poole/Getty Images: 98 (right); ©iStockphoto.com/fajean: 99; ©Charles C. Place/Getty Images: 101; ©IMAGEMORE Co., Ltd./Alamy: 102; ©iStockphoto.com/francisblack: 103; ©Comstock/Getty Images: 104; ©Ariel Skelley/Getty Images: 105; ©iStockphoto.com/VCNW: 106; ©David Young-Wolff/PhotoEdit Inc.: 107; ©Comstock/Getty Images: 108; ©iStockphoto.com/DorianPhotoInc: 109; ©Jim Wehtje/Getty Images: 110; ©Comstock/Getty Images: 112; ©Corbis Premium RF/Alamy: 113; ©Siede Preis/Getty Images: 115; ©MELBA PHOTO AGENCY/Alamy: 116; ©Stewart Cohen/Getty Images: 119; ©iStockphoto.com/monkeybusinessimages: 120; ©iStockphoto.com/solarseven: 121; ©Robert Struwe/Alamy: 122; ©Penrod Studios/Alamy: 123; ©Corbis: 124; ©Hisham Ibrahim/Alamy: 124 (inset); ©iStockphoto.com/EwaWysocka: 125; ©iStockphoto.com/tibor5: 127; ©Don Despain/www.rekindlephoto.com/Alamy: 128; ©iStockphoto.com/kassandra: 129; ©iStockphoto.com/amanalang: 130; ©Digital Vision/Getty Images: 131; ©Sharon Lowe/Alamy: 132; ©Comstock/Jupiterimages: 133 (left); ©Tim Pannell/Corbis/Getty Images: 133 (right); ©Jon Parker Lee/Alamy: 134; ©Pictorial Press Ltd/Alamy: 135; ©iStockphoto.com/tainted: 136; ©Image Source/Getty Images: 138; ©Blend Images/SuperStock: 140; ©Comstock/Jupiterimages: 142, 156; ©CORBIS: 152; ©Jim Esposito/Photolibrary: 154; ©Digital Vision/Getty Images: 156–157

ISBN 978-1-4531-1798-9

Copyright © 2016 Zaner-Bloser, Inc.

Zaner-Bloser, Inc.
1-800-421-3018
www.zaner-bloser.com

Printed in the United States of America

ZB Code 16

9 10 11 12 13 997 23 22 21 20 19

CONTENTS

Zaner-Bloser

Unit 4 Using What You Have Learned

This book will help you practice your writing skills. You will review manuscript writing. Then you will learn to write letters, words, and sentences in cursive.

Handwriting Tutor

Scan the **Handwriting Tutor** codes with a mobile device to watch handwriting videos.

Keys to Legibility

You will see the **Keys to Legibility** often in this book. The Keys name four things to think about that will help you make your writing **legible,** or easy to read. They are **Shape, Size, Spacing,** and **Slant**.

Handwriting Tutor

Stop and Check

When you see the **Stop and Check** sign in your book, stop writing. Circle the best letter or joining you wrote on that line. Evaluating what you wrote will help you become a better writer.

Handwriting Tutor

People use manuscript writing every day. Good manuscript writing is easy to read.

Be sure to place your paper in the correct position for manuscript when you write. That will help keep your writing straight up and down.

Writing Positions   Manuscript

If you write with your LEFT hand . . .

Place the paper like this.

Slant the paper as shown in the picture.

Rest both arms on the desk. Use your right hand to move the paper as you write.

Pull the pencil toward your left elbow when you write.

Hold the pencil like this.

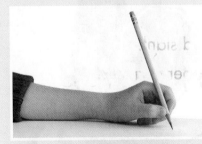

Hold the pencil with your thumb and first two fingers. Do not squeeze the pencil when you write.

If you write with your RIGHT hand . . .

Place the paper like this.

Handwriting Tutor

Place the paper straight in front of you.

Rest both arms on the desk. Use your left hand to move the paper as you write.

Pull the pencil toward the middle of your body when you write.

Hold the pencil like this.

Handwriting Tutor

Hold the pencil with your thumb and first two fingers. Do not squeeze the pencil when you write.

Keys to Legibility

Make your writing easy to read.

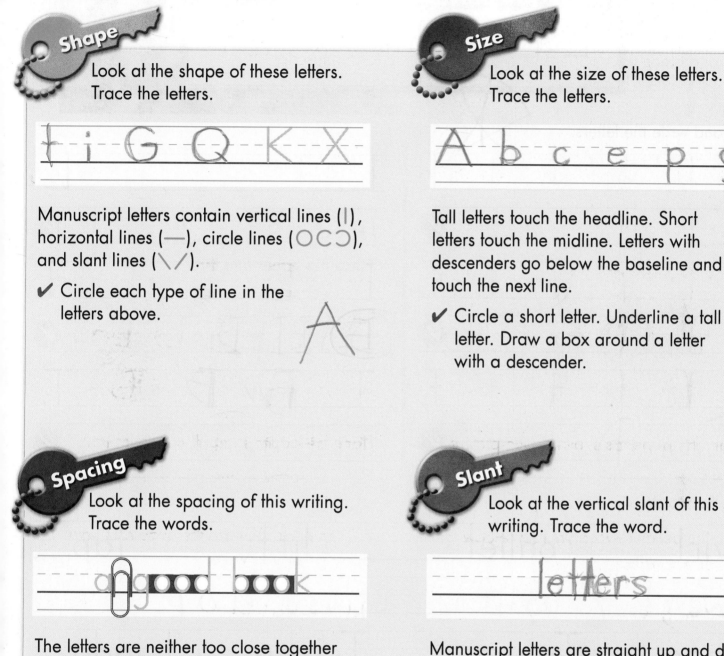

Shape

Look at the shape of these letters. Trace the letters.

fiGQKX

Manuscript letters contain vertical lines (│), horizontal lines (—), circle lines (○⊃), and slant lines (\/).

✔ Circle each type of line in the letters above.

Size

Look at the size of these letters. Trace the letters.

Abcepg

Tall letters touch the headline. Short letters touch the midline. Letters with descenders go below the baseline and touch the next line.

✔ Circle a short letter. Underline a tall letter. Draw a box around a letter with a descender.

Spacing

Look at the spacing of this writing. Trace the words.

a good book

The letters are neither too close together nor too far apart.

There is enough space for a paper clip between words.

✔ Use a paper clip or your little finger to measure the spacing between the words above.

Slant

Look at the vertical slant of this writing. Trace the word.

letters

Manuscript letters are straight up and down. To write with good slant:

1. Place your paper correctly.
2. Pull down in the proper direction.
3. Shift your paper as you write.

✔ Draw lines through the vertical strokes in the letters above. If your lines are straight, then the writing has good slant.

7

Manuscript Review

Trace and write the letters.

l l l l l l   L L L L L L

i i i i i i   I I I I I I

t t t t t t   T T T T T T

Write the words.

twirl   ballet   lift   tap

twirl   ballet   lift   tap

Isaac   Tanya   Teisha   Linda

Isaac   Tanya   Teisha   Linda

pointed toes

pointed toes

Shape

Circle your word that has the best vertical lines.

Handwriting Tutor

8

Trace and write the letters.

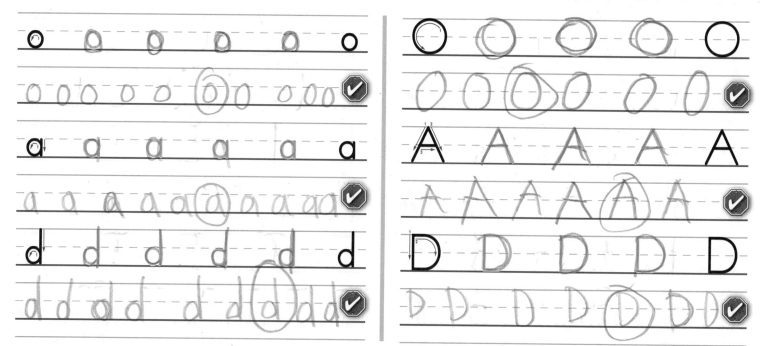

Write the words.

glove   hooray   double   baseball

glove   hooray   double   baseball

Don   Todd   Anna   Omar

Don   Todd   Anna   Omar

second base

second base

Trace and write the letters.

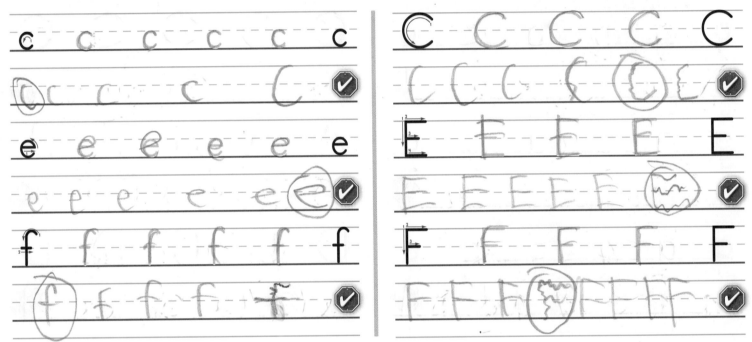

Write the words.

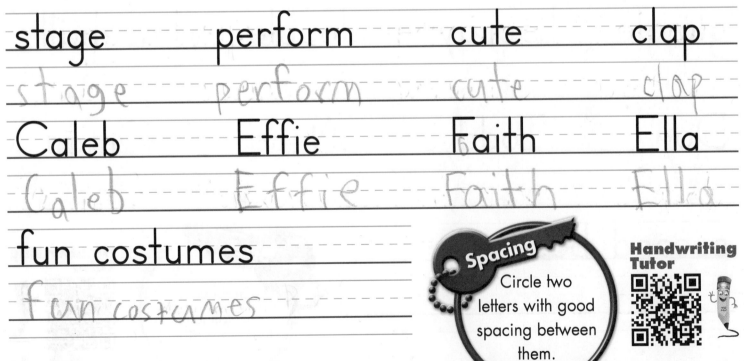

stage   perform   cute   clap

Caleb   Effie   Faith   Ella

fun costumes

Spacing
Circle two letters with good spacing between them.

Handwriting Tutor

10

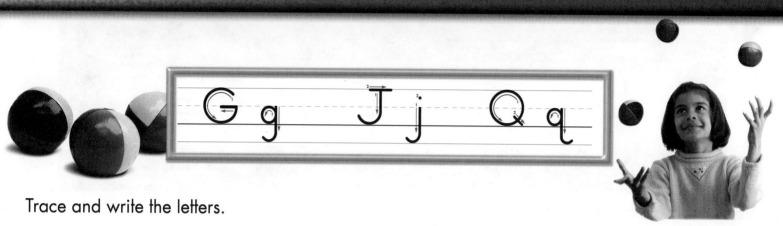

Trace and write the letters.

g g g g g g g
g g g g g g g ✓

j j j j j j j
j j j j j j ✓

q q q q q q q
q q q q q q q ✓

G G G G G G
G G G G G ✓

J J J J J J J
J J J ✓

Q Q Q Q Q Q
Q Q Q Q Q ✓

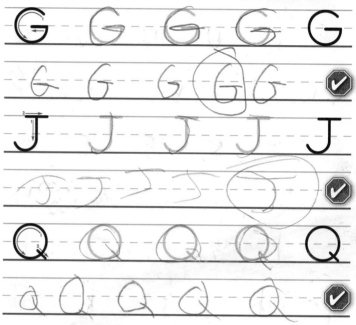

Write the words.

juggle   equipment   enjoy   quit
juggle   equipment   enjoy   quit

Jay   Ginny   Juan   Quito
Jay   Ginny   Juan   Quito

quick juggler
quick juggler

U u   S s   B b   P p

Trace and write the letters.

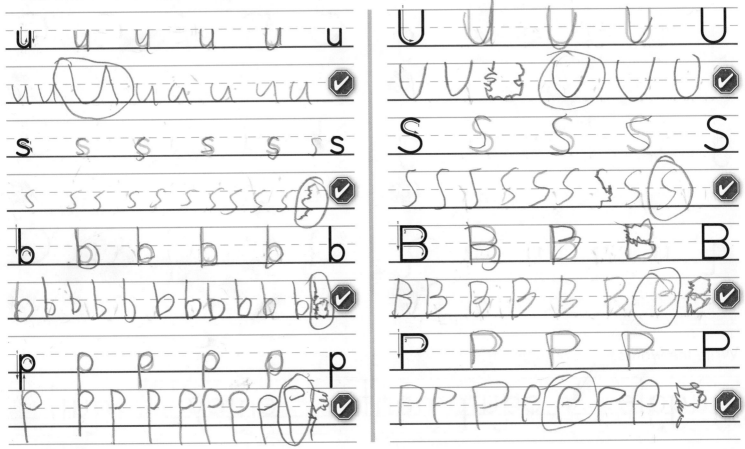

Write the words.

paint   use   splatter   brush

Pat Sam Bess

Shape

Circle the word you wrote that has the best circle lines.

Handwriting Tutor

Trace and write the letters.

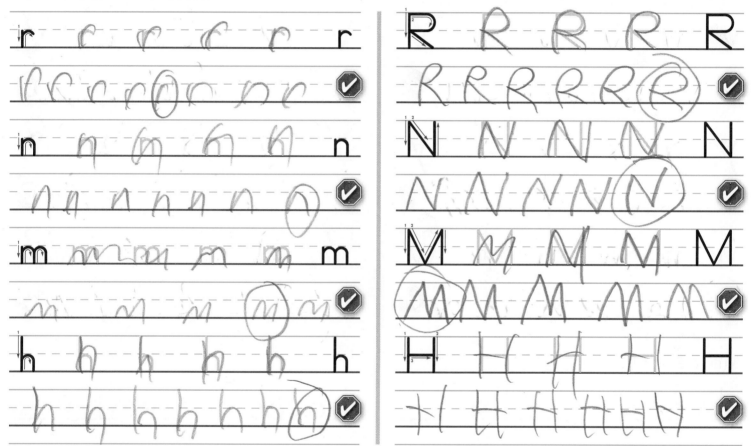

Write the words.

musician   song   rhythm   Nina

musician   song   rhythm   Nina

Mia   Ray   Hal

Mia   Ray

Handwriting Tutor

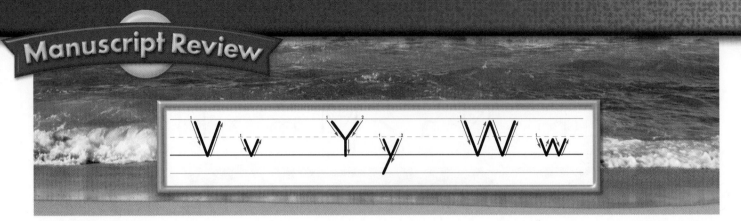

Trace and write the letters.

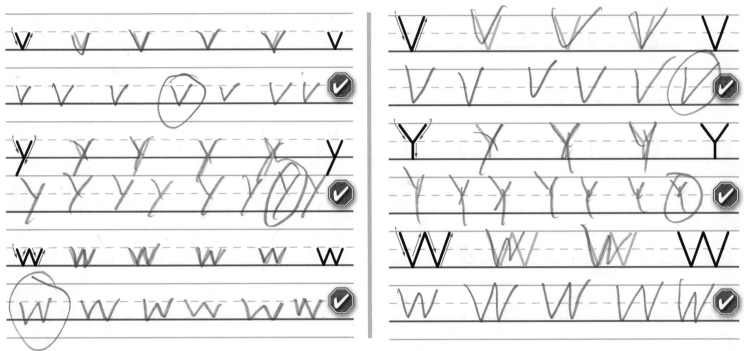

Write the words.

dive   swim   waves   water

Wyatt   Vaughn   Gwen   Yan

very sunny day

Spacing

Circle two letters with good spacing between them.

Handwriting Tutor

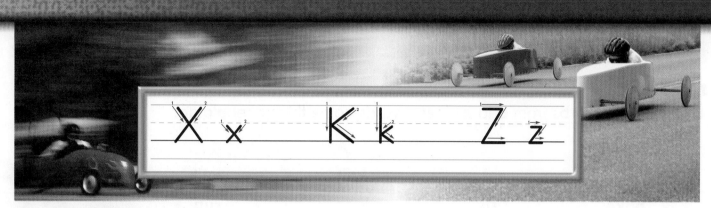

X x   K k   Z z

Trace and write the letters.

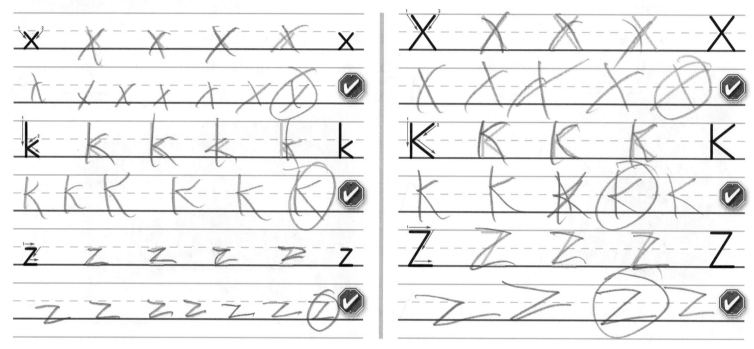

Write the words.

zone   extra   zoom   axle

zone   extra   zoom   axle

Karina   Xavier   Zack   Kate

Karina   Xavier   Zack   Kate

soapbox track

soapbox track

Slant
Circle your best word that is straight up and down.

Handwriting Tutor

Practice

Verbs Here are verbs from **a** to **z**. These words name things people do.

act	eat	knit	quit	
bake	fish	leap	run	
catch	giggle	march	sing	write
dance	hug	nap	throw	fix
	illustrate	observe	understand	yell
	jump	practice	visit	zoom

Circle four things you do. Then write four sentences.
Each sentence should include one of the verbs you circled.

Application

Writing a List Sometimes you write lists of things you have to do.

Things to Do

1. read my book

2. write a book report

3. illustrate it

4. color the cover

Write a list of things you plan to do soon.

1.

I'd Like To Be a Lighthouse

I'd like to be a lighthouse
    And scrubbed and painted white.
I'd like to be a lighthouse
    And stay awake all night
To keep my eye on everything
    That sails my patch of sea;
I'd like to be a lighthouse
    With the ships all watching me.

Rachel Field

I'd Like To Be a Lighthouse
I'd like to be a lighthouse
    And scrubbed and painted white.
I'd like to be a lighthouse
    And stay awake all night
To keep my eye on everything
    That sails my patch of sea;
I'd like to be a lighthouse
    With the ships all watching me.

Write the title and the poem in your best manuscript or cursive handwriting. Remember to leave space for margins.

Welcome to Cursive

You are writing very well.
Your manuscript letters look good.
Each letter stands straight up and down,
The way manuscript letters should.

You're ready to write a new way.
You're ready for cursive, at last!
Cursive writing is graceful,
Cursive writing is fast.

You are ready for cursive writing! As you begin, you will notice how cursive writing is different from manuscript writing. Look at these words.

ready   *ready*

Notice that the letters in the cursive word are joined together.

Notice that cursive writing slants forward.

Try it. Write some letters you know in cursive.

What else can you write in cursive? Write it here.

The pages in this book will help you learn to write cursive letters, words, and sentences.

Cursive Letters and Numerals

Circle the uppercase cursive letters that are your initials.
Underline the lowercase cursive letters that are in your name.
Draw a box around the uppercase cursive letter that begins the name of your state.

Now take a closer look.
Which manuscript and cursive letters are most alike? Draw stars beside them.

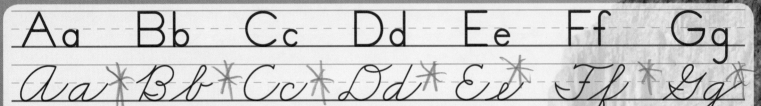

Hh Ii Jj Kk Ll Mm

Hh Ii Jj Kk Ll Mm

Nn Oo Pp Qq Rr Ss Tt

Nn Oo Pp Qq Rr Ss Tt

Uu Vv Ww Xx Yy Zz

Uu Vv Ww Xx Yy Zz

Circle the cursive numeral that tells your age.

1 2 3 4 5 6 7 8 9 10

1 2 3 4 5 6 7 (8) 9 10

Reading Cursive Writing

Look at the orange manuscript lowercase letter.
Circle the cursive lowercase letter that matches it.

a	a	b	c	d	e	f
g	d	e	f	g	h	i
n	j	k	l	m	n	o
r	p	q	r	s	t	u
z	u	v	w	x	y	z

Look at the orange manuscript uppercase letter.
Circle the cursive uppercase letter that matches it.

B	A	B	C	D	E	F
E	D	E	F	G	H	I
M	I	J	K	L	M	N
Q	O	P	Q	R	S	T
Y	U	V	W	X	Y	Z

Read the name of a sport written in manuscript.
Circle the matching word written in cursive.

baseball	*baseball*	*football*	*soccer*
volleyball	*diving*	*volleyball*	*skating*
tennis	*hockey*	*skiing*	*tennis*
football	*football*	*hockey*	*basketball*
skating	*swimming*	*skating*	*tennis*

Read the name of a sport written in cursive.
Write the name in manuscript.

tennis

basketball

soccer

ice skating

Cursive

Left-Handed Writers

Sit like this.

Sit comfortably.

Lean forward a little.

Keep your feet flat on the floor.

Place the paper like this.

Slant the paper as shown in the picture.

Rest both arms on the desk. Use your right hand to shift the paper as you write.

Pull the pencil toward your left elbow when you write.

Hold the pencil like this.

Hold the pencil with your thumb and first two fingers.

Keep your first finger on top.

Bend your thumb and keep it on the side.

Do not squeeze the pencil when you write.

Right-Handed Writers

Sit like this.

Sit comfortably.
Lean forward a little.
Keep your feet flat on the floor.

Place the paper like this.

Handwriting Tutor

Slant the paper as shown in the picture.

Rest both arms on the desk. Use your left hand to shift the paper as you write.

Pull the pencil toward the middle of your body when you write.

Hold the pencil like this.

Handwriting Tutor

Hold the pencil with your thumb and first two fingers.

Keep your first finger on top.

Bend your thumb and keep it on the side.

Do not squeeze the pencil when you write.

Handwriting Tutor

Undercurve

An **undercurve** is one of the basic strokes used to write cursive letters.

An undercurve stroke swings up.

Trace an undercurve stroke at the beginning of each lowercase letter.

b   e   f   h   i   j   k

l   p   r   s   t   u   w

Trace an undercurve stroke at the beginning of each uppercase letter.

B   G   L   P   R   S

Trace and write undercurve strokes.

Downcurve

A **downcurve** is one of the basic strokes used to write cursive letters.

A downcurve stroke dives down.

Trace a downcurve stroke at the beginning of each lowercase letter.

a   c   d   g   o   q

Trace a downcurve stroke at the beginning of each uppercase letter.

A   C   D   E   O

Trace and write downcurve strokes.

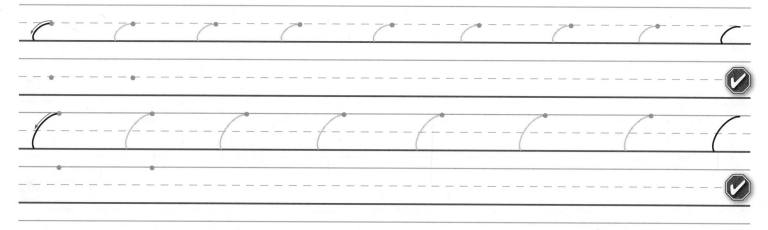

Overcurve

An **overcurve** is one of the basic strokes used to write cursive letters.

An overcurve stroke bounces up.

Trace an overcurve stroke at the beginning of each lowercase letter.

m   n   v   x   y   z

Trace an overcurve stroke at the beginning of each uppercase letter.

I   J   Q

Trace and write overcurve strokes.

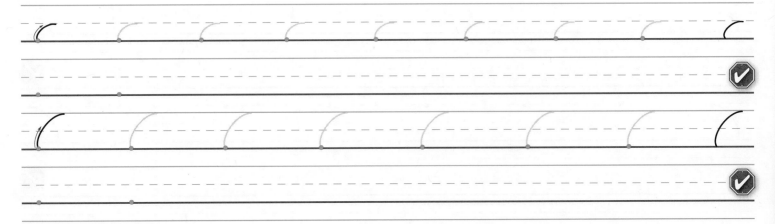

Slant

A **slant** is one of the basic strokes
used to write cursive letters.

A slant stroke slides.

Trace a slant stroke in each lowercase letter.

a   b   d   f   g   h   i

j   k   l   m   t   u   y

Trace a slant stroke in each uppercase letter.

A   B   K   P   R   U   X   Y

Trace and write slant strokes.

Keys to Legibility

Slant

Spacing

Size

Shape

You will learn to write lowercase cursive letters. As you write, pay attention to the four Keys to Legibility.

Shape

There are four basic strokes in cursive writing.
Be sure to write each letter with good basic strokes.

undercurve	downcurve	overcurve	slant

Circle each letter that has an undercurve beginning.

w   d   c   h   w

Circle each letter that has a downcurve beginning.

a   j   p   g   s

Circle each letter that has an overcurve beginning.

b   n   r   v   z

Circle each letter that has a slant stroke.

c   k   l   m   o

32

Size

Look at the size of each letter. Use the guidelines to help you make each letter the correct size.

Tall letters touch the headline.

b   d   h

Short letters touch the midline.

a   m   g   w

Some letters have descenders that go below the baseline and touch the next headline.

f   g   y

Circle the tall letters.

a   c   d   e   f   g   h   k

Circle the short letters.

l   n   d   g   s   t   u   w

Circle the letters that have descenders.

p   g   s   t   u   x   y   z

33

Keys to Legibility

Slant
Spacing
Size
Shape

Handwriting Tutor

To help make your lowercase cursive letters easy to read, pay attention to the four Keys to Legibility.

Spacing

Look at the spacing between letters and words.

There should be space for O between letters.

bectotoon sgpaacionng

There should be space for \ between words.

word\spacing

Circle the word that has good letter spacing.

spacing spacing spacing

Circle the line that has good word spacing.

word spacing

word spacing

wordspacing

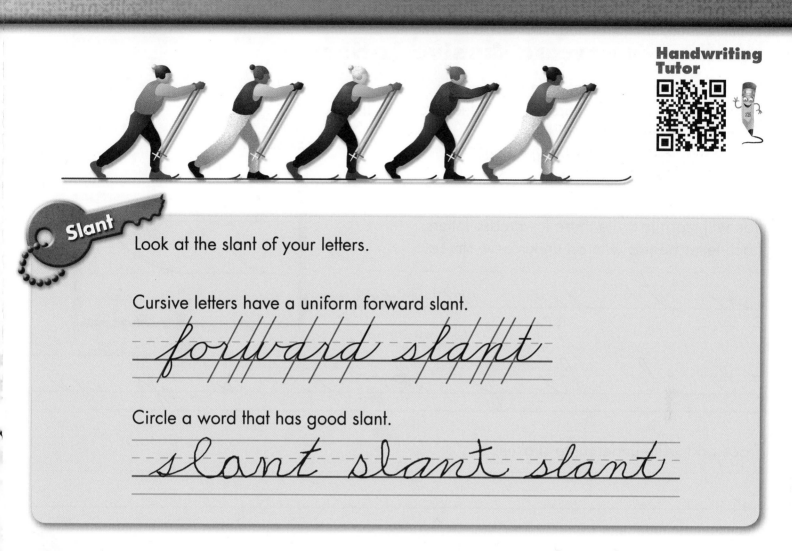

Slant

Look at the slant of your letters.

Cursive letters have a uniform forward slant.

forward slant

Circle a word that has good slant.

slant slant slant

To write with good slant:

POSITION PULL SHIFT

- Check your paper **position**.
- **Pull** your downstrokes in the proper direction.
- **Shift** your paper as you write.

If you are left-handed . . .

pull toward your left elbow.

If you are right-handed . . .

pull toward your midsection.

Writing Lowercase Cursive Letters

Let's begin with lowercase letters.
As you learn to write in cursive, you'll learn to read it, too.
You will learn to write each letter.
Then you'll join letters and write words.

Undercurve Letters

You will learn to write these lowercase letters.
Each letter begins with an undercurve stroke.

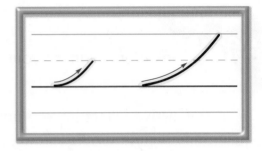

i t u w e

l b h f k r s j p

Trace and write undercurve strokes.

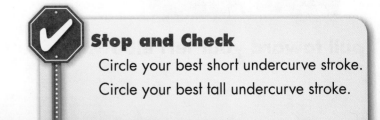

Stop and Check
Circle your best short undercurve stroke.
Circle your best tall undercurve stroke.

Downcurve Letters

You will learn to write these lowercase letters.
Each letter begins with a downcurve stroke.

a   d   g   o   c   q

Trace and write downcurve strokes.

Overcurve Letters

You will learn to write these lowercase letters.
Each letter begins with an overcurve stroke.

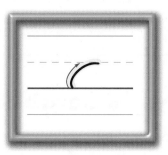

n   m   y   x   v   z

Trace and write overcurve strokes.

Undercurve Letters

On the next pages, you will write lowercase letters that begin with an undercurve stroke. Undercurves swing up.

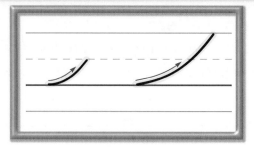

Each of these letters begins with an undercurve stroke.

i   t   u   w   e   l   b

h   f   k   r   s   j   p

Trace and write undercurve strokes.

Keys to Legibility

Make your undercurve letters easy to read. Pay attention to the four Keys.

Shape

Undercurves swing up.

Size

Undercurves may be short or tall.

i p   *l h*

short letters   tall letters

Spacing

Swing wide to join a letter that ends with an undercurve to a letter that begins with an undercurve. That way your letters will have good spacing.

see the bee

Slant

Position your paper as shown on pages 26–27. That way your undercurve letters will have good slant.

38

The letter *i* has an undercurve beginning and ending.

insect

insect

Trace and write.

i   i   i   i   i   i   i

Join *i* and *i*. The ending stroke of the first letter begins the second letter.

ii   ii   ii   ii   ii   ii

Handwriting Tutor

Stroke description to guide letter formation at home:
1. Undercurve.
2. Slant; undercurve. Lift.
3. Dot.

39

The letter t begins with a tall undercurve stroke.

test tubes

test tubes

Trace and write.

t t t t t t t

Join t and other letters. Notice the undercurve-to-undercurve joinings.

it it it it it it

tt tt tt ti ti ti

Handwriting Tutor

Stroke description to guide letter formation at home:

1. Undercurve.
2. Slant; undercurve. Lift.
3. Slide right.

Stop and Check

Circle your best t.

40

The letter *u* has three undercurve strokes.

umbrellas

umbrellas

Trace and write.

uu *uu* *uu* *uu* *uu* *uu* *uu*

Join *u* and other letters. Notice the undercurve-to-undercurve joinings.

ut *ui* *uit* *iu* *tu*

tutu *tutu* *tutu*

Handwriting Tutor

Stroke description to guide letter formation at home:
1. Undercurve.
2. Slant; undercurve.
3. Slant; undercurve.

Size

Circle your best short letter.

41

The letter *w* has an undercurve beginning and a checkstroke (⌣) ending.

W *w*

water wheel
water wheel

Trace and write.

w   w   w   w   w   w   w

Join *w* and other letters. The checkstroke joins two letters.

wu   wi   wt   tw   uw

Write the word.

wit   wit   wit   wit

Stroke description to guide letter formation at home:

1. Undercurve.
2. Slant; undercurve.
3. Slant; undercurve.
4. Checkstroke.

✓ **Stop and Check**
Circle your best *w*.

42

e *e*

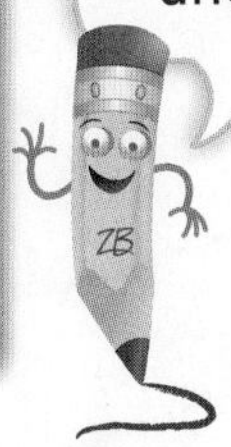

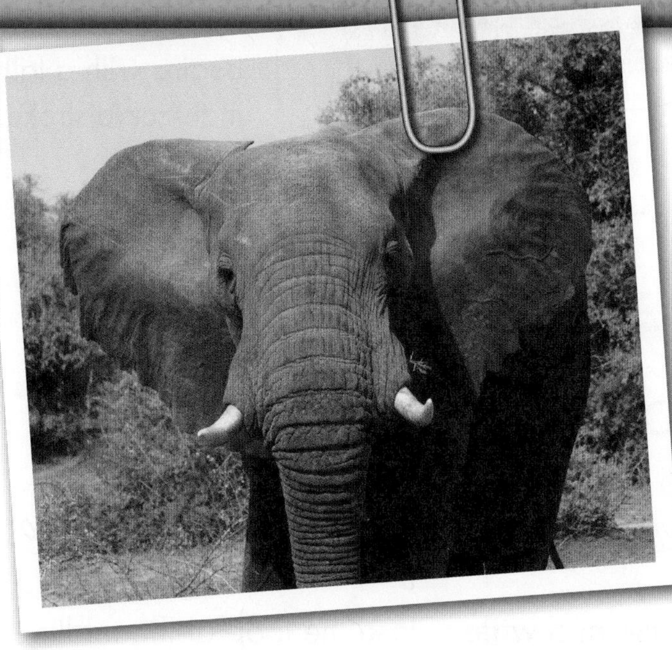

elephant ears

elephant ears

Trace and write.

e   e   e   e   e   e   e   e

Join *e* and other letters.

ew   eu   ei   et   te   ie

Write the words.

tie   we   tweet   wet

$\mathcal{l}$

The letter $\mathcal{l}$ begins with a tall undercurve stroke.

lots of lumber
lots of lumber

Trace and write. Close the loop at the midline.

$\mathcal{l}$ $\mathcal{l}$ $\mathcal{l}$ $\mathcal{l}$ $\mathcal{l}$ $\mathcal{l}$ $\mathcal{l}$ $\mathcal{l}$

Join $\mathcal{l}$ and other letters.

li   le   lt   il   el   wl

Write the words.

lit   let   tell   will

Handwriting Tutor

Stroke description to guide letter formation at home:

l. Undercurve; loop back; slant; undercurve.

Stop and Check
Circle your best $\mathcal{l}$.

44

b

b

The letter *b* has an undercurve beginning and a checkstroke ending.

banana bunch

banana bunch

Trace and write.

b   b   b   b   b   b   b   b

Join *b* and other letters. Notice the checkstroke-to-undercurve joining.

be   bi   bl   bu   ib   eb

Write the words.

bell   bill   tube   web

Handwriting Tutor

b

Stroke description to guide letter formation at home:

1. Undercurve; loop back; slant; undercurve.
2. Checkstroke.

Slant

Circle a letter you wrote that has good slant.

45

h *h*

The letter *h* begins and ends with an undercurve stroke.

herd of horses

herd of horses

Trace and write.

h   h   h   h   h   h   h

Join *h* and other letters.

he   hi   hu   wh   th   ht

Write the words.

hub   while   the   with

Handwriting Tutor

Stroke description to guide letter formation at home:
1. Undercurve; loop back; slant.
2. Overcurve; slant; undercurve.

Stop and Check
Circle your best *h*.

The letter *f* begins and ends with an undercurve stroke.

flip-flops

flip-flops

Trace and write.

f f f f f f f f

Join *f* and other letters.

fl   fi   fe   ft   ife

Write the words.

full   beef   fit   left

Handwriting Tutor

Stroke description to guide letter formation at home:

1. Undercurve; loop back; slant; loop forward.
2. Undercurve.

Shape

Circle your best letter that has an undercurve beginning.

k k

The letter *k* begins with a tall undercurve stroke.

black kittens

black kittens

Trace and write.

k   k   k   k   k   k   k

Join *k* and other letters.

ke   ki   kl   ike   eek

Write the words.

kit   bike   week   kite

Handwriting Tutor

Stroke description to guide letter formation at home:
1. Undercurve; loop back; slant.
2. Overcurve; curve forward; curve under.
3. Slant right; undercurve.

48

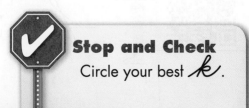

Stop and Check
Circle your best *k*.

r

The letter *r* begins and ends with an undercurve stroke.

red rooster

red rooster

Trace and write.

r   *r*   *r*   *r*   *r*   *r*

Join *r* and other letters.

rl   *ru*   *ir*   *tr*   *wr*   *ire*

Write the words.

rule   *reel*   *write*   *true*

Handwriting Tutor

Stroke description to guide letter formation at home:
1. Undercurve.
2. Slant right.
3. Slant; undercurve.

Size

Circle your best short letter.

S $\mathscr{s}$

The letter $\mathscr{s}$ begins and ends with an undercurve stroke.

steep slope

steep slope

Trace and write.

$\mathscr{s}$ $\mathscr{s}$ $\mathscr{s}$ $\mathscr{s}$ $\mathscr{s}$ $\mathscr{s}$ $\mathscr{s}$

Join $\mathscr{s}$ and other letters.

se   *sk*   *sl*   *sw*   *ss*   *st*

Write the words.

sweet   *skis*   *bus*   *wrist*

Handwriting Tutor

Stroke description to guide letter formation at home:
1. Undercurve.
2. Curve down and back.
3. Undercurve.

Stop and Check
Circle your best $\mathscr{s}$.

j j

The letter *j* begins with an undercurve and ends with an overcurve.

jelly jars

jelly jars

Trace and write.

j   j   j   j   j   j   j

Join *j* and other letters. The overcurve becomes an undercurve that begins the next letter.

je   ji   ju   jui   ej

Write the words.

jets   just   jewels

Handwriting Tutor

Stroke description to guide letter formation at home:
1. Undercurve.
2. Slant; loop back; overcurve. Lift.
3. Dot.

Spacing

Circle a word you wrote that has good joinings.

51

p

The letter *p* begins and ends with an undercurve stroke.

purple plums

purple plums

Trace and write.

p   p   p   p   p   p   p

Join *p* and other letters.

pi   pe   pl   pr   ph   sp

Write the words.

put   push   beep   spell

Handwriting Tutor

Stroke description to guide letter formation at home:

1. Undercurve.
2. Slant; loop back; overcurve; curve back.
3. Undercurve.

Stop and Check
Circle your best *p*.

52

Write the joinings and words.

Undercurve-to-Undercurve Joining

The undercurve ending swings wide to begin the following letter.

hi   kit   list   tree

Checkstroke-to-Undercurve Joining

The checkstroke ending dips deep to begin the following letter.

we   wi   bus   blue

Overcurve-to-Undercurve Joining

The overcurve ending crosses at the baseline and turns into a wide undercurve.

ji   ju   jet   just

Stop and Check

Circle three words you wrote that have good joinings.

53

i t u w e l b
h f k r s j p

Write these rhyming words.

keep peep jeep beep

jet pet set wet

hill bill fill will

true blue few flew

Homophones

Homophones are words that sound alike but are spelled differently. They have different meanings, too.

see
sea

Write these homophone pairs.

fur fir   *be bee*

peer pier   *flew flu*

its it's   *wheel we'll*

their there   *sweet suite*

blue blew   *few phew!*

There are five words spelled incorrectly in the short story below. On the guidelines, write the misspelled words correctly and in cursive. Writing the words again will help you remember them.

On a small farm, there lived a mouse named Louisa. She slept under a pyle of hay in the barn. She poot her food behind a loose board in the wall. One day, she found that her food was gone. She was shure she had hidden a big piece of cheese their. She was so hungry her stomach was starting to hirt. So Louisa set out to discover who stole her cheese.

1. _____

2. _____

3. _____

4. _____

5. _____

The more you practice writing in cursive, the easier it will be!

Read this postcard. The writer made his letters small enough to fit the space on the postcard.

Handwriting Tutor

message   address

Dear Paul,

    I am in Washington, D.C. We're at the National Air and Space Museum. I wish you were here.

            Brian

Paul Parker
22 Baker Street
Chicago, IL 60657

USA

Write Brian's postcard, or write one of your own. Use manuscript writing. Remember to write a message and a mailing address. Make your writing fit the space.

USA

Write the poem.
Make your writing easy to read.

pets true

will keep

true blue

his sleep

58

Write your own poem.
Be sure to leave space for margins.

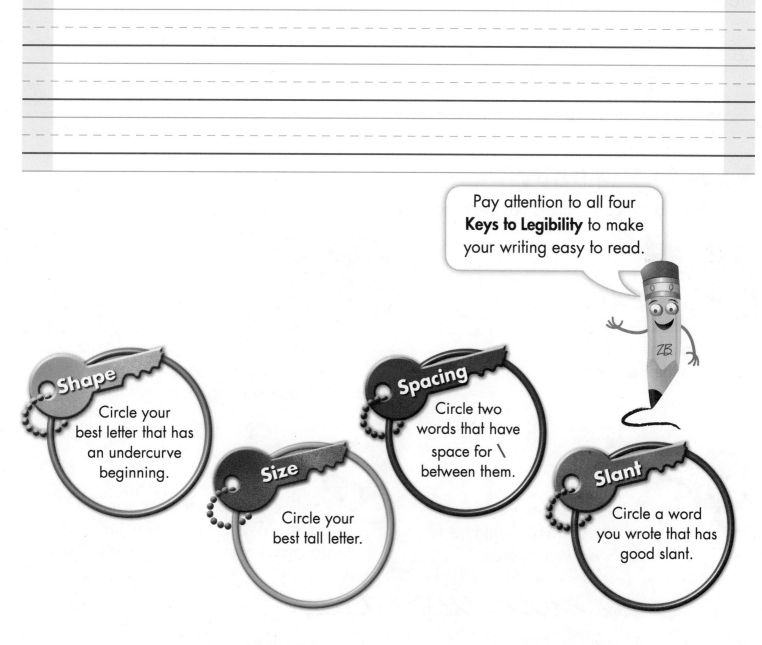

Pay attention to all four **Keys to Legibility** to make your writing easy to read.

Shape
Circle your best letter that has an undercurve beginning.

Size
Circle your best tall letter.

Spacing
Circle two words that have space for \ between them.

Slant
Circle a word you wrote that has good slant.

Downcurve Letters

On the next pages, you will write lowercase letters that begin with a downcurve stroke. Downcurves begin at the midline and dive down to the baseline.

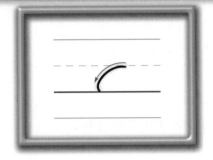

Each of these letters begins with a downcurve stroke.

Trace and write downcurve strokes.

Keys to Legibility

Make your downcurve letters easy to read. Pay attention to the four Keys.

Shape

Downcurve lowercase letters begin on the midline and dive down to the baseline.

Size

Use the headline, midline, baseline, and descender space as your guides. That way your letters will be the right size.

Spacing

There should be space for O between letters. There should be space for \ between words.

Slant

Position your paper as shown on pages 26–27. That way your downcurve letters will have good slant.

The letter a begins with a downcurve stroke.

arrow

arrow

Trace and write. Notice the undercurve ending.

a a a a a a a a

Join a and other letters. Notice the undercurve-to-downcurve joining.

aa   ea   ra   al   aw   as

Write the words.

treat   all   awhile   ask

Handwriting Tutor a

Stroke description to guide letter formation at home:
1. Downcurve; undercurve.
2. Slant; undercurve.

Shape

Circle your best downcurve beginning.

d d

The letter *d* has a downcurve beginning.

desert

desert

Trace and write.

d d d d d d d d

Join *d* and other letters.

da de di dd ad ide

Write the words.

desert added wide

Stroke description to guide letter formation at home:

1. Downcurve; undercurve.
2. Slant; undercurve.

Stop and Check
Circle your best *d*.

g g

The letter *g* begins with a downcurve and ends with an overcurve.

globe

globe

Trace and write.

g   g   g   g   g   g   g   g

Join *g* and other letters. Notice the overcurve-to-downcurve joining.

ga   gg   gi   gh   gr   gl

Write the words.

gift   grade   wiggle

Handwriting Tutor

g

Stroke description to guide letter formation at home:

1. Downcurve; undercurve.
2. Slant; loop back; overcurve.

Size

Circle your best letter that has a descender.

63

O o

The letter *o* begins with a downcurve and ends with a checkstroke.

oranges

oranges

Trace and write.

o   o   o   o   o   o   o   o

Join *o* and other letters. Notice the checkstroke-to-downstroke joining.

od   oa   oo   ot   or   oll

Write the words.

other   orders   boots

Stroke description to guide letter formation at home:
1. Downcurve; undercurve.
2. Checkstroke.

✓ **Stop and Check**
Circle your best *o*.

C C C

The letter C has a downcurve beginning and an undercurve ending.

clouds

clouds

Trace and write.

C C C C C C C C C

Join C and other letters.

ce   cl   cr   ck   uce

Write the words.

called   cried   could

Handwriting Tutor

C

Stroke description to guide letter formation at home:
1. Downcurve; undercurve.

Spacing

Circle a word you wrote that has good joinings.

65

q q

The letter *q* begins with a downcurve stroke.

quarters

quarters

Trace and write.

q q q q q q q q q

Join *q* and other letters.

qu quo qua qui que

Write the words.

quick quarters quote

Handwriting Tutor

Stroke description to guide letter formation at home:

1. Downcurve; undercurve.
2. Slant; loop forward.
3. Undercurve.

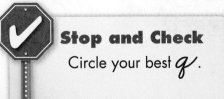

Stop and Check
Circle your best *q*.

66

Write the joinings and words.

Undercurve-to-Downcurve Joining
The undercurve swings wide to form the top of the downcurve of the next letter.

ea   ra   sa   ed   do   call

Overcurve-to-Downcurve Joining
The overcurve crosses at the baseline and then continues up and wide to form the top of the downcurve letter.

ga   ja   gg   go   joke

Checkstroke-to-Downcurve Joining
The checkstroke ending swings wide to form the top of the downcurve letter.

oa   wa   oo   boo   bog

Stop and Check
Circle your three best joinings.

67

a   d   g   o   c   q

Write the names of breakfast foods.

quiche   cereal   eggs

toast   bagel   bread

Write the phrases.

a quart of grape juice

a good breakfast

Nouns

Nouns are naming words. The nouns on this page name vegetables.
Write the words.

squash carrots peppers

lettuce cabbages leeks

potatoes peas broccoli

Complete the sentences. Leave space for margins.

I like to eat

I don't like to eat

Stop and Check
Circle your best word.

69

Learning cursive will help you write more quickly.
This can be good for writing a list of things to do.

take a bath

get dressed

pick apples

make a pie

The more you practice writing in cursive, the easier it will be!

Overcurve Letters

On the next pages, you will write lowercase letters that begin with an overcurve stroke. Overcurves begin at the baseline and bounce up to the midline.

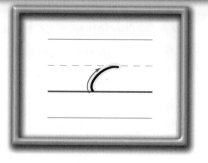

Each of these letters begins with an overcurve stroke.

Trace and write overcurve strokes.

Keys to Legibility

Make your overcurve letters easy to read. Pay attention to the four Keys.

Shape

Overcurve lowercase letters begin at the baseline and bounce up to the midline.

Size

Use the midline, baseline, and descender space as your guides. That way, your letters will be the right size.

Spacing

Swing wide on the last stroke of each letter to allow for good spacing as you join letters.

Slant

Remember that cursive letters have a consistent forward slant.

even slant

n *n*

neighborhood

neighborhood

Trace and write.

n   n   n   n   n   n   n

Join *n* and other letters.

nn   sn   an   na   nd   ne

Write the words.

newspaper   band   often

Handwriting Tutor

n

Stroke description to guide letter formation at home:

1. Overcurve; slant.
2. Overcurve; slant; undercurve.

Stop and Check

Circle your best *n*.

m m

The letter m has three overcurve strokes.

messy mouth

messy mouth

Trace and write.

m m m m m m m

Join m and other letters.

me mi ma ime ame

Write the words.

mile slammed might

Handwriting Tutor

m

Stroke description to guide letter formation at home:

1. Overcurve; slant.
2. Overcurve; slant.
3. Overcurve; slant; undercurve.

Slant

Circle a word you wrote that has good slant.

y Y

The letter *y* begins and ends with an overcurve stroke.

young puppy

young puppy

Trace and write.

y   y   y   y   y   y   y

Join *y* and other letters.

ym   yo   ye   ty   oy

Write the words.

yellow   your   city   buy

Handwriting Tutor

Stroke description to guide letter formation at home:
1. Overcurve; slant; undercurve.
2. Slant; loop back; overcurve.

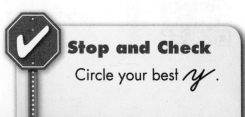

Stop and Check

Circle your best *y*.

74

X x

The letter x begins with an overcurve stroke.

exit the taxi

exit the taxi

Trace and write.

x x x x x x x

✓

✓

Join x and other letters.

xy   *xa*   *ix*   *ex*   *ax*   *ox*

✓

Write the words.

xylophone   *exit*   *fix*

✓

Handwriting Tutor

x

Stroke description to guide letter formation at home:

1. Overcurve; slant; undercurve. Lift.
2. Slant.

Shape

Circle your best letter that has a good slant stroke.

75

V $\mathscr{N}$

The letter $\mathscr{N}$ begins with an overcurve and ends with a checkstroke.

volcano

volcano

Trace and write.

$\mathscr{N}$　$\mathscr{N}$　$\mathscr{N}$　$\mathscr{N}$　$\mathscr{N}$　$\mathscr{N}$　$\mathscr{N}$

Join $\mathscr{N}$ and other letters. Notice the checkstroke-to-overcurve joining.

vy va vi ove ive ave

Write the words.

envy　very　visitor

Handwriting Tutor

$\mathscr{N}$

Stroke description to guide letter formation at home:

1. Overcurve; slant; undercurve.
2. Checkstroke.

✔ **Stop and Check**
Circle your best $\mathscr{N}$.

Z

The letter *z* begins and ends with an overcurve stroke.

zoo zebras

zoo zebras

Trace and write.

z   z   z   z   z   z   z

Join *z* and other letters.

zy   zi   ze   za   ize   oze

Write the words.

zebra   zipper   zigzag

Handwriting Tutor

Stroke description to guide letter formation at home:

1. Overcurve; slant.
2. Overcurve; curve down; loop; overcurve.

Size

Circle your best letter that has a descender.

77

n   m   y   x   v   z

Write these color words.

maroon   lime   orange

neon green   tangerine

violet   lavender   silver

yellow   ivory   azure

pink   a color mix

Complete this sentence in cursive.

My favorite color is _____.

Adjectives

What a great day for a picnic!
Write these phrases that describe foods you might find at a picnic.

marvelous gigantic salad

amazing icy lemonade

tasty tuna sandwiches

yummy yellow mustard

juicy pink melon

excellent cherry pie

Stop and Check
Circle your best word.

Write this to-do list.
Make your writing easy to read.

organize toys in basement

ride skateboard

read one book or more

write school book report

have best sleepover ever

Write a to-do list of things you need to do soon.
Be sure to include a few things you want to do, too.

Is your writing easy to read?

Shape Circle your best letter that has an overcurve beginning.

Size Circle your best short letter. Underline your best tall letter.

Spacing Circle two words that have space for \ between them.

Slant Circle a word you wrote that has good slant.

Lowercase Letters

a   b   c   d   e   f   g

n   o   p   q   r   s   t

Write these lowercase letters in cursive.

i t u w

e l b h f

k r s j p

a d g o c q

n m y x v z

Write these words in cursive.

cozy

happy

swift

great

young

mixed

lively

brave

juicy

quick

h   *i*   *j*   *k*   *l*   *m*

u   *v*   *w*   *x*   *y*   *z*

Change the order of the letters to write a new word.

deal	pat	late
lead		
ate	trap	pool
tens	dear	limes
nap	ant	gulp
own	tone	

My writing has good **Shape** ☐
My writing has good **Size** ☐
My writing has good **Spacing** ☐
My writing has good **Slant** ☐

83

Write each joining. Then write the word.

Undercurve-to-Undercurve

ri   *ride*   *ti*   *time*

Undercurve-to-Downcurve

ea   *eat*   *mo*   *moon*

Undercurve-to-Overcurve

ry   *cry*   *az*   *amaze*

Overcurve-to-Undercurve

ju   *just*   *ye*   *yell*

Overcurve-to-Downcurve

ga   *gate*   *yo*   *you*

Overcurve-to-Overcurve

zy   *dizzy*   *gy*   *foggy*

Checkstroke-to-Undercurve

wr   *wrote*   *os*   *most*

Checkstroke-to-Downcurve

ba   *back*   *vo*   *voices*

Checkstroke-to-Overcurve

om   *home*    *ov*   *over*

Cursive Numerals

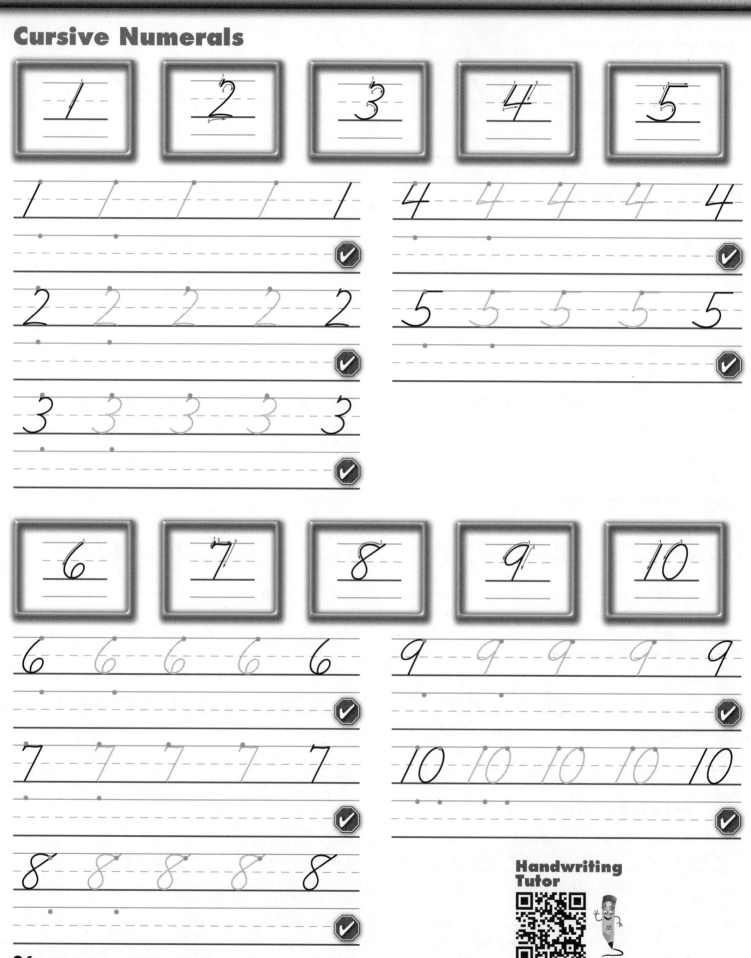

Handwriting
Tutor

Sam's Busy Day

9:00	Reading
10:30	Math
11:30	Social Studies
12:30	Lunch
1:15	Gym
2:00	Science
3:00	School's Out
4:00	Homework
5:00	Violin Lesson
6:00	Dinner
7:00	Free Time
9:00	Sleep

1. When does Sam start his homework? _____

2. When does Sam eat lunch? _____

3. When does Sam have math? _____

4. When does Sam go home? _____

5. When does Sam go to sleep? _____

6. When does Sam have his violin lesson? _____

Read this recipe for a fruit salad. The writer made her letters small enough to fit the space on the recipe card.

Grandma's Fruit Salad
1. chop peaches and apples
2. slice strawberries and bananas
3. add both red and green grapes
4. dip all fruit in pineapple juice
5. mix together in a bowl and serve

Copy the recipe here. Use your best manuscript writing.
Make your writing fit the space.

The steps for this recipe are out of order. Write the steps in the correct order on the recipe card below. Use your best manuscript writing, and make your writing fit the space.

Grandpa's Tortilla Casserole
5. pour salsa and sprinkle cheese over top
1. to begin, fill tortilla with shredded cheese
6. cook until cheese has melted
4. sprinkle cheese between rolled tortillas
3. stuff and roll more tortillas until dish is full
2. roll up tortilla and place in cooking dish

Did you use the space wisely? Is your manuscript writing easy to read?

Writing Uppercase Cursive Letters

Downcurve Letters

You will learn to write these uppercase letters.
Each letter has a downcurve stroke.

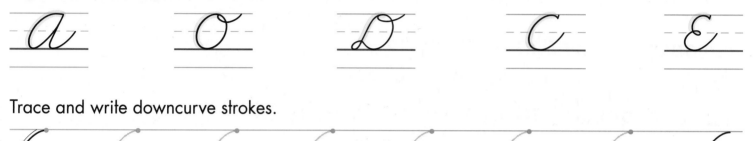

Trace and write downcurve strokes.

Curve Forward Letters

You will learn to write these uppercase letters.
Each letter begins with a curve forward stroke.

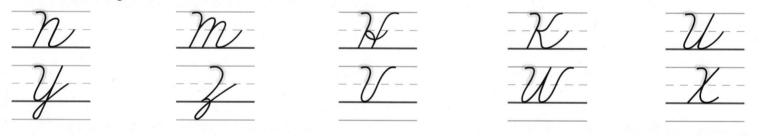

Trace and write curve forward-slant strokes.

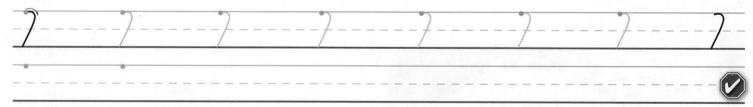

Stop and Check

Circle your best downcurve stroke.

Circle your best curve forward-slant stroke.

Overcurve Letters

You will learn to write these uppercase letters. Each letter begins with an overcurve stroke.

Trace and write overcurve strokes.

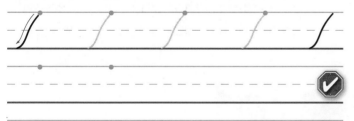

Undercurve-Loop Letters

You will learn to write these uppercase letters. Each letter begins with an undercurve and a loop stroke.

Trace and write undercurve-loop strokes.

Doublecurve Letters

You will learn to write these uppercase letters. Each letter has a doublecurve stroke.

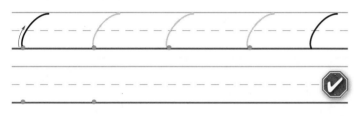

Trace and write doublecurve strokes.

Undercurve-Slant Letters

You will learn to write these uppercase letters. Each letter begins with an undercurve and a slant stroke.

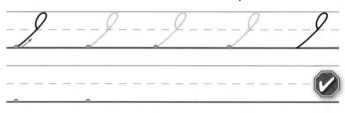

Trace and write undercurve-slant strokes.

Downcurve Letters

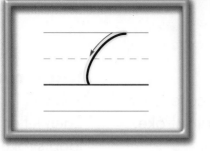

You will learn to write these uppercase letters. Each letter has a downcurve stroke.

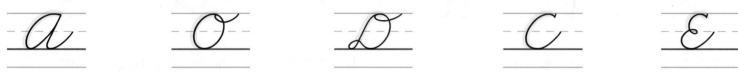

Trace and write downcurve strokes.

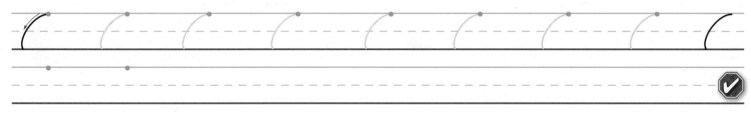

Keys to Legibility

Make your downcurve letters easy to read. Pay attention to the four Keys.

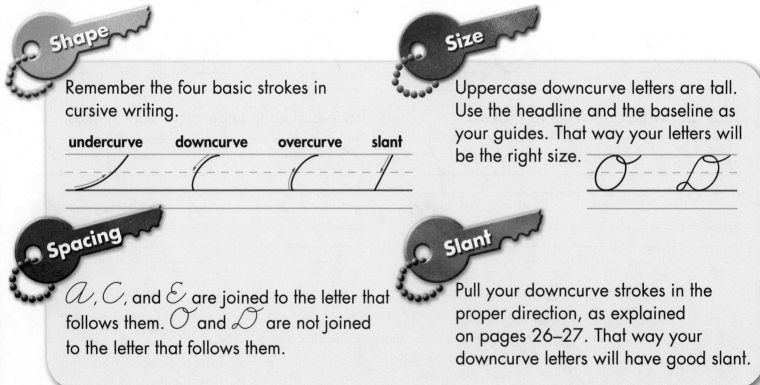

Shape

Remember the four basic strokes in cursive writing.

undercurve   downcurve   overcurve   slant

Size

Uppercase downcurve letters are tall. Use the headline and the baseline as your guides. That way your letters will be the right size.

Spacing

𝒶, 𝒞, and ℰ are joined to the letter that follows them. 𝒪 and 𝒟 are not joined to the letter that follows them.

Slant

Pull your downcurve strokes in the proper direction, as explained on pages 26–27. That way your downcurve letters will have good slant.

A a

The letter *a* begins with a downcurve stroke.

Angelo visits the Alamo.

Angelo visits the Alamo.

Trace and write.

a a a a a a a

a is joined to the letter that follows. Write words that begin with *a*.

America   April   Aleisha

Write the sentence.

Angelo is amazed.

Handwriting Tutor

a

Stroke description to guide letter formation at home:

1. Downcurve; undercurve.
2. Slant; undercurve.

Spacing

Circle your best joining.

O O

Olivia loves October.

Olivia loves October.

Trace and write.

O O O O O O O

O is not joined to the letter that follows. Write words that begin with *O*.

Oregon   Ohio   October

Write the sentence.

Olivia likes cool weather.

Handwriting Tutor

Stroke description to guide letter formation at home:

1. Downcurve; undercurve; loop; curve right.

Stop and Check

Circle your best *O*.

D

The letter *D* begins with a downcurve stroke.

Dylan and Dan are best friends.

Dylan and Dan are best friends.

Trace and write.

D   D   D   D   D   D

D is not joined to the letter that follows. Write words that begin with *D*.

Delaware   December   Dr.

Write the sentence.

Dylan shares with Dan.

Handwriting Tutor

Stroke description to guide letter formation at home:

1. Downcurve; loop; curve down and up; loop; curve right.

Slant

Circle a word you wrote that has good slant.

95

C C

The downcurve in *C* follows a short slant stroke.

CRAYON

Crayons are on Cara's desk.

Crayons are on Cara's desk.

Trace and write.

C   C   C   C   C   C   C

C is joined to the letter that follows. Write words that begin with *C*.

California   Colorado   Cara

Write the sentence.

Crayons are colorful.

Handwriting Tutor

Stroke description to guide letter formation at home:
1. Slant.
2. Downcurve; undercurve.

96

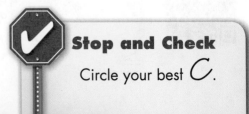

Stop and Check

Circle your best *C*.

E   *E*

The letter *E* ends with an undercurve stroke.

Emma visits England.

Emma visits England.

Trace and write.

E   E   E   E   E   E   E   E

E is joined to the letter that follows. Write words that begin with *E*.

England   English   Earth

Write the sentence.

Emma is excited.

Handwriting Tutor

E

Stroke description to guide letter formation at home:

1. Slant.
2. Downcurve; loop; downcurve; undercurve.

Shape

Circle your best letter that has a downcurve beginning.

97

A O D C E

Write names for a guest list.

Chris Chu   David Allen

Olivia Ames   Alex Olmos

Chip Dodd   Ellen Avila

Craig Estes   Emilia Cruz

Write the names of your classmates that begin with these letters.

Come One, Come All!
Celebrate Arbor Day

At: Chris Edson's house
Address: 5 Ocean Avenue

Date: April 29
Don't bring any treats.

Writing an Invitation

Write the invitation. Leave space for margins.

Stop and Check

Circle your best uppercase letter.

99

Curve Forward Letters

You will learn to write these uppercase letters. Each letter begins with a curve forward stroke.

Trace and write curve forward-slant strokes.

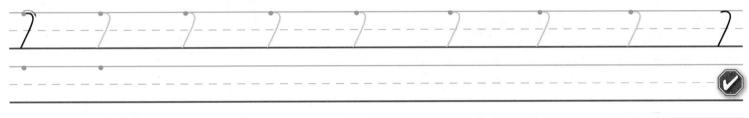

Keys to Legibility

Make your curve forward letters easy to read. Pay attention to the four Keys.

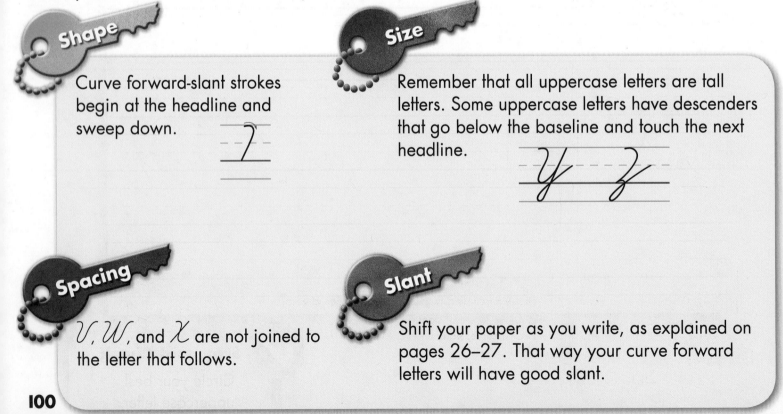

Shape
Curve forward-slant strokes begin at the headline and sweep down.

Size
Remember that all uppercase letters are tall letters. Some uppercase letters have descenders that go below the baseline and touch the next headline.

Spacing
𝒱, 𝒲, and 𝒳 are not joined to the letter that follows.

Slant
Shift your paper as you write, as explained on pages 26–27. That way your curve forward letters will have good slant.

N n

The letter *n* begins with a curve forward-slant stroke.

Nate looks for Neptune.

Nate looks for Neptune.

Trace and write.

n n n n n n n

n **is joined to the letter that follows. Write words that begin with** *n*.

November   Nevada   Nat

Write the sentence.

Neptune is hard to see.

Handwriting Tutor

n

Stroke description to guide letter formation at home:
1. Curve forward; slant.
2. Overcurve; slant; undercurve.

Size

Circle your best tall letter.

M m

The letter *m* begins with curve forward and ends with undercurve.

My birthday is in May.

My birthday is in May.

Trace and write.

m   m   m   m   m   m   M

M is joined to the letter that follows. Write words that begin with *m*.

Montana   Monday   May

Write the sentence.

Mom will make a cake.

Handwriting Tutor

Stroke description to guide letter formation at home:
1. Curve forward; slant.
2. Overcurve; slant.
3. Overcurve; slant; undercurve.

Stop and Check
Circle your best *m*.

Hunter surfs in Honolulu.

Hunter surfs in Honolulu.

Trace and write.

H is joined to the letter that follows. Write words that begin with *H*.

Hawaii   Houston   Hello!

Write the sentence.

Hunter likes high waves.

Handwriting Tutor

Stroke description to guide letter formation at home:
1. Curve forward; slant. Lift.
2. Curve back; slant.
3. Retrace; loop; curve right.

Spacing

Circle a word you wrote that has good joinings.

K K

The letter K begins with curve forward and ends with undercurve.

Keira does not feel OK.

Keira does not feel OK.

Trace and write.

K K K K K K K

K is joined to the letter that follows. Write words that begin with K.

Kansas   Kentucky   Ken

Write the sentence.

Keira has a cold.

Handwriting Tutor

Stroke description to guide letter formation at home:
1. Curve forward; slant. Lift.
2. Doublecurve.
3. Curve forward and down; undercurve.

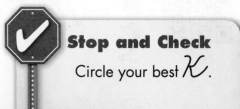

Stop and Check
Circle your best K.

U u

The letter $\mathcal{U}$ begins with a curve forward stroke.

Uma likes the U.S.A.

Uma likes the U.S.A.

Trace and write.

$\mathcal{U}$ $\mathcal{U}$ $\mathcal{U}$ $\mathcal{U}$ $\mathcal{U}$ $\mathcal{U}$ $\mathcal{U}$

$\mathcal{U}$ is joined to the letter that follows. Write words that begin with $\mathcal{U}$.

Uncle Uli   Utah

Write the sentence.

Uma visits from Uruguay.

Handwriting Tutor

Stroke description to guide letter formation at home:

1. Curve forward; slant; undercurve.
2. Slant; undercurve.

Slant

Circle a letter you wrote that has good slant.

105

Y *Y*

The letter *Y* ends with an overcurve stroke.

Yasmin is in Yellowstone.

Yasmin is in Yellowstone.

Trace and write.

Y   Y   Y   Y   Y   Y   Y

Y is joined to the letter that follows. Write words that begin with *Y*.

Yosemite   *Yorktown*

Write the sentence.

Yellowstone is a big park.

Stroke description to guide letter formation at home:
1. Curve forward; slant; undercurve.
2. Slant; loop back; overcurve.

106

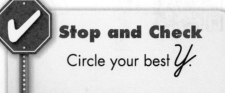
Stop and Check
Circle your best *Y*.

Z

Zip! Zoe zooms past.

Zip! Zoe zooms past.

Trace and write.

Z   Z   Z   Z   Z   Z   Z

Z is joined to the letter that follows. Write words that begin with *Z*.

Zion   Zack   Zelda

Write the sentence.

Zoe wears a helmet.

Handwriting Tutor

Z

Stroke description to guide letter formation at home:
1. Curve forward and down; slant.
2. Overcurve; curve down; loop; overcurve.

Shape

Circle your best letter that has an overcurve ending.

The letter $\mathcal{V}$ begins with a curve forward stroke.

Violet enjoys Valentine's Day.

Violet enjoys Valentine's Day.

Trace and write.

$\mathcal{V}$ is not joined to the letter that follows. Write words that begin with $\mathcal{V}$.

Vermont   Virginia   Venus

Write the sentence.

Violet gives valentines.

Handwriting Tutor

Stroke description to guide letter formation at home:
1. Curve forward; slant; undercurve; overcurve.

Stop and Check
Circle your best $\mathcal{V}$.

W W

The letter *W* begins with a curve forward stroke.

Will visits the White House.

Will visits the White House.

Trace and write.

W W W W W W W

W is not joined to the letter that follows. Write words that begin with *W*.

Washington   Wednesday

Write the sentence.

Will takes a tour.

Handwriting Tutor

W

Stroke description to guide letter formation at home:
1. Curve forward; slant; undercurve.
2. Slant; undercurve; overcurve.

Size

Circle your best tall letter.

$\mathcal{X}$ $\quad$ $\mathcal{X}$

The letter $\mathcal{X}$ begins with a curve forward stroke.

Xavier has an X-ray.

Xavier has an X-ray.

Trace and write.

$\mathcal{X}$ $\quad$ $\mathcal{X}$ $\quad$ $\mathcal{X}$ $\quad$ $\mathcal{X}$ $\quad$ $\mathcal{X}$ $\quad$ $\mathcal{X}$ $\quad$ $\mathcal{X}$

$\mathcal{X}$ is not joined to the letter that follows. Write words that begin with $\mathcal{X}$.

Xena $\qquad$ *Xander* $\qquad$ *X-ray*

Write the sentence.

Xavier sits still.

Handwriting Tutor

$\mathcal{X}$

Stroke description to guide letter formation at home:

1. Curve forward; slant; undercurve. Lift.
2. Slant.

Stop and Check
Circle your best $\mathcal{X}$.

Write the joinings.

Joining *N* and *M*

N and *M* are joined to the letter that follows. The undercurve ending must be wide enough to allow room for joining to the next letter.

Ne　　*Mi*　　*No*　　*Ma*　　*My*

Joining *H* and *K*

H and *K* are joined to the letter that follows. The loop in *H* swings across the letter and slightly down to allow room for joining to the next letter.

He　　*Ki*　　*Ha*　　*Ko*　　*Hu*

Joining *U*, *Y*, and *Z*

U, *Y*, and *Z* are joined to the letter that follows. The overcurve ending in *Y* and *Z* crosses at the baseline, then continues up and wide to form the next letter.

Ue　　*Ya*　　*Zo*　　*Ye*　　*Zu*

The cursive letters *V*, *W*, and *X* are not joined to the letter that follows.

Stop and Check

Circle your three best joinings.

111

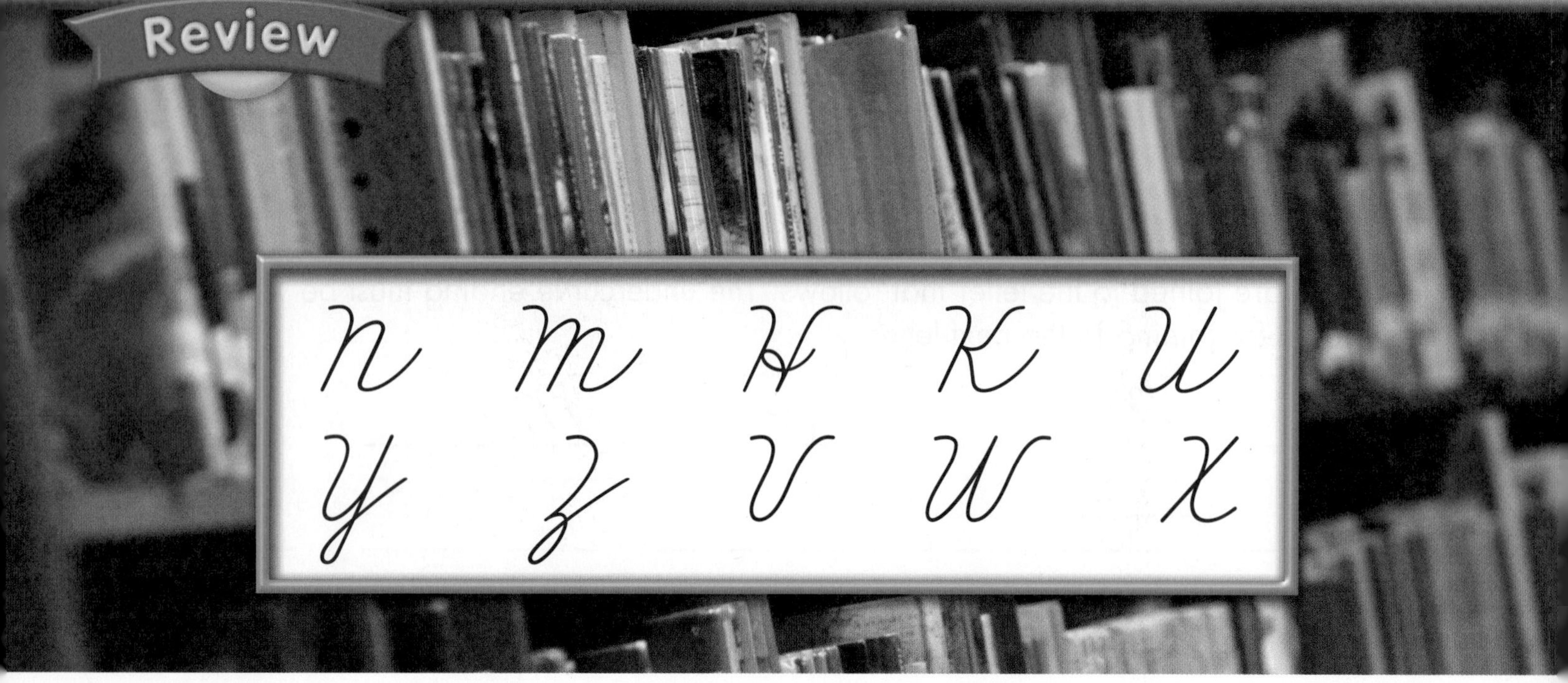

n m H K U
Y Z V W X

Here are titles of books you may have read. Write the titles. Underline them.

<u>*Under My Nose*</u>

<u>*When We Were Very Young*</u>

<u>*17 Kings and 42 Elephants*</u>

<u>*Henry Huggins*</u>

<u>*Zella, Zack, and Zodiac*</u>

Henry Huggins meets a funny dog. He likes the dog right away. While on their way to Henry's house, they have lots of adventures. What a great book! You should read it.

Complete this book review in *cursive* handwriting. Leave room for margins.

Title: Henry Huggins

Author: Beverly Cleary

What Happened:

Stop and Check

Circle your best uppercase letter.

The more you practice writing in cursive, the easier it will be!

In the Real World

Learning cursive will help you write more quickly. This can be good for writing a phone message. Write this note in your best cursive writing.

A lady named Val called. Do you want to join the exercise group? Bring a friend along. Call 555-9843. She is in a hurry to sign people up. Look at the website for an example of the exercises you'll do.

On most forms, you see the words **Please print**.
Use manuscript to complete the information form below.

Handwriting Tutor

School Library
Information Form

Please print.

Name _____

Grade _____

Favorite book _____

_____

Write which kinds of books you like to read.

history   science fiction   biography
mystery   folktales   plays

_____

_____

Check how many books you would like
to take out each week.

☐ 1   ☐ 2   ☐ 3   ☐ 4

How many times a week do you like to visit the library?

_____

On which day would you like to come for reading club?

_____

Write the paragraph about the sun.
Make your writing easy to read. Pay attention to the margins.

Earth circles the sun.

Our sun is a large star.

A star is a really hot ball of gas that gives off light and heat.

Write your own paragraph about the sun.
Be sure to leave space for margins.

Our sun is very important because

Is your writing easy to read?

Shape
Circle your best letter that has a downcurve beginning.

Size
Circle your best tall letter.

Spacing
Circle two words that have space for \ between them.

Slant
Circle a word you wrote that has good slant.

Overcurve and Doublecurve Letters

You will learn to write these uppercase letters.
Each letter begins with an overcurve stroke.

I   *J*   *Q*

Trace and write overcurve strokes.

You will learn to write these uppercase letters.
Each letter has a doublecurve stroke.

T   *F*

Trace and write doublecurve strokes.

Keys to Legibility

Make your overcurve and doublecurve letters easy to read.

Shape
Overcurve strokes begin at the baseline and sweep up. Doublecurves begin at the headline and curve down.

Size
Use the headline, midline, baseline, and descender space as your guides. That way your letters will be the right size.

Spacing
There should be space for O between letters. There should be space for O between sentences.

Slant
Position your paper as shown on pages 26–27. That way your overcurve and doublecurve letters will have good slant.

I I

The letter *I* begins with an overcurve stroke.

Ina loves Italian food.

Ina loves Italian food.

Trace and write.

I   I   I   I   I   I   I

I is not joined to the letter that follows. Write words that begin with *I*.

Idaho   Illinois   Iowa

Write the sentence.

Ina traveled to Italy.

Handwriting Tutor

Stroke description to guide letter formation at home:
1. Overcurve; curve down and up.
2. Retrace; curve right.

Spacing

Circle your best joining.

J j

The letter *J* begins and ends with an overcurve stroke.

Jamal loves July 4th.

Jamal loves July 4th.

Trace and write.

J J J J J J J J

J is joined to the letter that follows. Write words that begin with *J*.

January   June   Jupiter

Write the sentence.

July 4th parades are fun.

Handwriting Tutor

J

Stroke description to guide letter formation at home:

I. Overcurve; slant; loop back; overcurve.

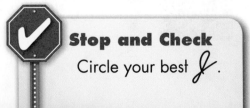

Stop and Check
Circle your best *J*.

Q Q

The letter Q begins with an overcurve stroke.

Quinn saw Queensland.

Quinn saw Queensland.

Trace and write.

Q   Q   Q   Q   Q   Q   Q

Q is not joined to the letter that follows. Write words that begin with Q.

Quentin   Quimby   Quito

Write the sentence.

Where is Queensland?

Stroke description to guide letter formation at home:
1. Curve back; overcurve; curve down; retrace; curve forward; curve under.

Slant

Circle a word you wrote that has good slant.

T T

The letter *T* has a doublecurve stroke.

Tsai is from Taipei.

Tsai is from Taipei.

Trace and write.

T   T   T   T   T   T   T   T

T is not joined to the letter that follows. Write words that begin with *T*.

Tuesday   Thursday

Write the sentence.

Taipei is in Taiwan.

Handwriting Tutor

Stroke description to guide letter formation at home:

1. Slant.
2. Curve forward and right. Lift.
3. Doublecurve; curve up.
4. Retrace; curve right.

122

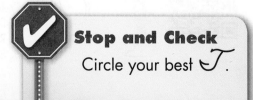

Stop and Check
Circle your best *T*.

F F

The letter *F* has a doublecurve stroke.

Flamingos flock to Florida.

Flamingos flock to Florida.

Trace and write.

F   F   F   F   F   F   F

F is not joined to the letter that follows. Write words that begin with *F*.

Flint   Friday   February

Write the sentence.

Frank lives in Florida.

Handwriting Tutor

Stroke description to guide letter formation at home:
1. Slant.
2. Curve forward and right. Lift.
3. Doublecurve; curve up.
4. Retrace; curve right. Lift.
5. Slide right.

Shape

Circle your best letter that has a doublecurve.

123

I J Q T F

Write the sentence.

I read about presidents.

Write these names of American presidents.

Third President: *Thomas Jefferson*

Sixth President: *John Quincy Adams*

Tenth President: *John Tyler*

Thirteenth President: *Millard Fillmore*

Writing Facts

Jupiter is a large planet.
Io is a moon of Jupiter.
Earth has one moon.
The sun is just a star.
Fixed stars are far off.
Quasars are big and shiny.

Write the facts about space in *cursive* handwriting. Leave room for margins.

Stop and Check
Circle your best word. 125

Undercurve-Loop and Undercurve-Slant Letters

You will learn to write these uppercase letters.
Each letter begins with an undercurve and a loop stroke.

Trace and write undercurve-loop strokes.

You will learn to write these uppercase letters.
Each letter begins with an undercurve and a slant stroke.

Trace and write undercurve-slant strokes.

Keys to Legibility

Make your undercurve-loop and undercurve-slant letters easy to read.

Shape
An undercurve stroke can begin at the baseline or the midline.

Size
Use the headline, midline, baseline, and descender space as your guides.
That way your letters will be the right size.

Spacing
R is joined to the letter that follows. Swing wide to join to the next letter. That way your letters will have good spacing.

Slant
Cursive letters have a consistent forward slant.

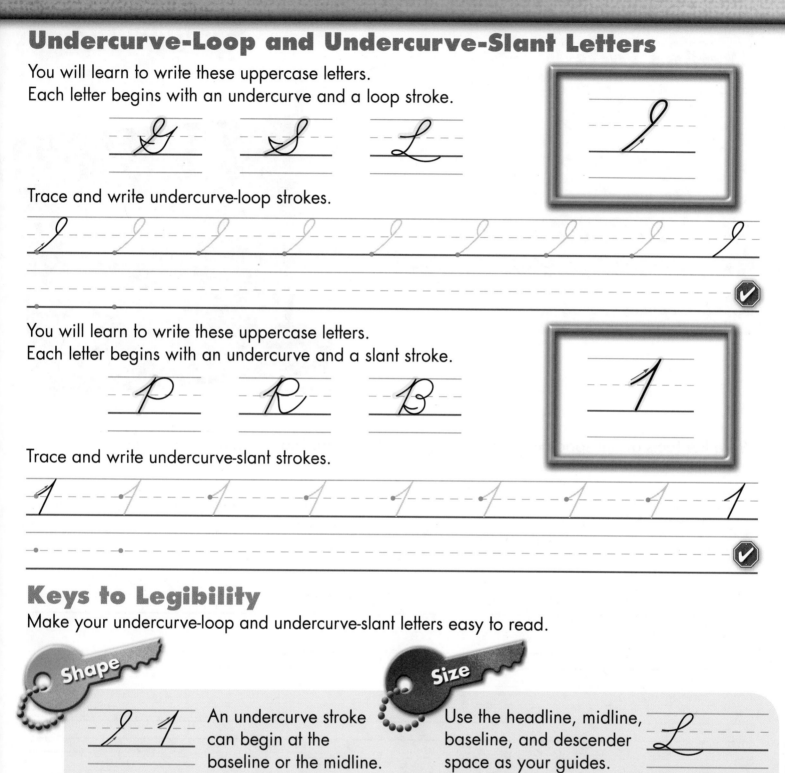

126

G   G

The letter *G* begins with an undercurve-loop stroke.

Gil eats a Georgia peach.

Gil eats a Georgia peach.

Trace and write.

G   G   G   G   G   G   G

G is not joined to the letter that follows. Write words that begin with *G*.

Georgia   Glendale   Greta

Write the sentence.

Gil grows great peaches.

Handwriting Tutor

Stroke description to guide letter formation at home:

1. Undercurve; loop; curve forward.
2. Doublecurve; curve up.
3. Retrace; curve right.

Size

Circle your best tall letter.

127

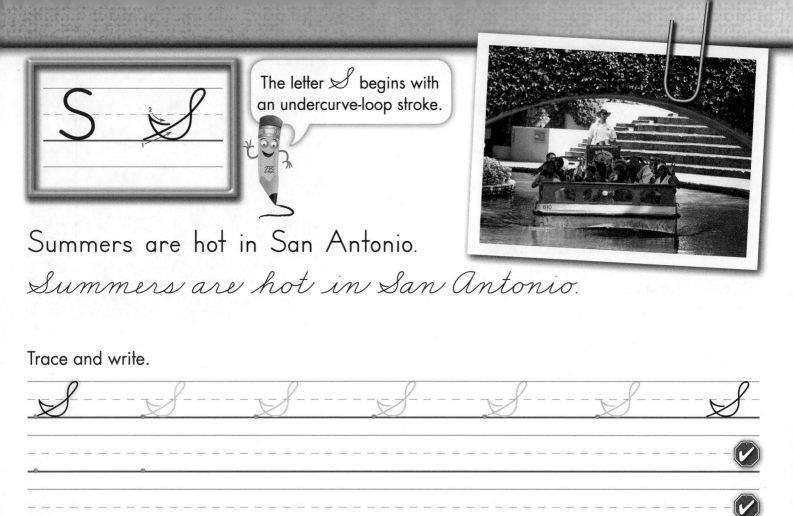

S   *S*

The letter *S* begins with an undercurve-loop stroke.

Summers are hot in San Antonio.

Summers are hot in San Antonio.

Trace and write.

S   *S*   *S*   *S*   *S*   *S*   *S*

S is not joined to the letter that follows. Write words that begin with *S*.

Saturday Sunday Sam

Write the sentence.

Sophie goes to the pool.

Handwriting Tutor

Stroke description to guide letter formation at home:
1. Undercurve; loop; curve down and up.
2. Retrace; curve right.

Stop and Check
Circle your best *S*.

The letter *L* begins with an undercurve-loop stroke.

Lisa sails on Lake Erie.

Lisa sails on Lake Erie.

Trace and write.

L   L   L   L   L   L   L

✓

✓

L is not joined to the letter that follows. Write words that begin with *L*.

Louisiana   Little League

✓

Write the sentence.

Lake Erie is fresh water.

✓

Handwriting Tutor

L

Stroke description to guide letter formation at home:

I. Undercurve; loop; curve down;
   loop; curve under.

Spacing

Circle your best joining.

129

P P

The letter *P* begins with an undercurve-slant stroke.

Pastries in Paris are pretty.

Pastries in Paris are pretty.

Trace and write.

P   P   P   P   P   P   P

P is not joined to the letter that follows. Write words that begin with *P*.

Pennsylvania   *Pluto*

Write the sentence.

Papa is a pastry chef.

Handwriting Tutor

Stroke description to guide letter formation at home:

1. Undercurve.
2. Slant.
3. Retrace; curve forward and back.

130

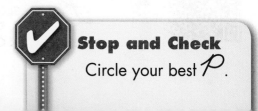

Stop and Check
Circle your best *P*.

R R

The letter *R* begins with an undercurve-slant stroke.

Roller coasters thrill Ryan.

Roller coasters thrill Ryan.

Trace and write.

R R R R R R R R

R is joined to the letter that follows. Write words that begin with *R*.

Rhode Island   Richmond

Write the sentence.

Ryan likes Ferris wheels!

Handwriting Tutor

Stroke description to guide letter formation at home:
1. Undercurve.
2. Slant.
3. Retrace; curve forward and back.
4. Curve forward; undercurve.

Slant

Circle a letter you wrote that has good slant.

B B

The letter *B* begins with an undercurve-slant stroke.

Brady loves Boston.

Brady loves Boston.

Trace and write.

B   B   B   B   B   B   B

B is not joined to the letter that follows. Write words that begin with *B*.

Boston   Boise   Bismarck

Write the sentence.

Boston ball games are fun.

Handwriting Tutor

Stroke description to guide letter formation at home:
1. Undercurve.
2. Slant.
3. Retrace; curve forward; loop; curve forward and back.
4. Retrace; curve right.

132

Stop and Check
Circle your best *B*.

Remember! These letters are not joined to the letter that follows.

B D F G I L O P Q S T V W X

Write the names of special days in *cursive*.

Groundhog Day

Father's Day

Thanksgiving

Labor Day

Independence Day

Washington's Birthday

Veterans Day

Pet Owner's Day

Lincoln's Birthday

School Librarian Day

G S L P R B

Here are some authors whose books you may have read. Write their names.

Brian Pinkney   Jan Brett

Cynthia Ryland   Dr. Seuss

Maurice Sendak

Paul Goble   Lewis Carroll

Eve Bunting   Hugh Lofting

Writing About a Book Character

I love to read exciting Dr. Doolittle stories. He is a doctor who can talk to the animals. He understands what they say. He helps them feel better.

Write the paragraph about Dr. Doolittle. Leave space for margins.

Stop and Check
Circle your best word.

135

Cursive Writing

In the Real World

> The Mitten by Jan Brett
> It is a snowy winter day. A
> boy drops his mitten. One by one,
> eight animals climb inside.
> There is always enough room.
> But when the bear sneezes, all
> the animals bounce back out.

Use cursive to write the book summary. Leave space for margins.

Uppercase Cursive Review

Write these uppercase letters in *cursive*.

A B C D E F G H I

J K L M N O P Q R

S T U V W X Y Z

Remember! These letters are joined to the letter that follows.

A C E H J K M N R U Y Z

Write these song titles in *cursive*.

"Kumbaya"

"Yankee Doodle"

"Clementine"

"My Bonnie"

"Are You Sleeping?"

"Home on the Range"

"John Henry"

Keys to Legibility

Write these tips for healthy eating.
Make your writing easy to read.

Drink enough water.

Always wash vegetables.

Cook meat well.

Support local farmers!

Finish this letter stating your opinion about eating well.
Be sure to leave space for margins.

Dear _____,
It is important to eat
well because

Shape
Circle your best letter that has an undercurve beginning.

Size
Circle your best tall letter.

Spacing
Circle two words that have space for \ between them.

Is your writing easy to read?

Slant
Circle a word you wrote that has good slant.

Read the personal narrative.
Write the narrative in your best manuscript.
Remember to leave space for margins.

> *Last summer was great. My father and mother took me to visit our family in Mexico. I had never been to another country. I got to see how my little cousins live. Those children have so much fun!*

Read the diary entry in cursive.
Use manuscript to write the passage below.
Remember to leave space for margins.

Sometimes I like to paint.
I am done with this picture.
I painted a big ship sailing
below a black, starry sky.
My mom thought it was beautiful.

Is your manuscript writing easy to read?

Friendly Letter

Use cursive to write the letter.
Write as quickly and neatly as you can.
Be sure to leave room for margins.

Dear Papa and Mama,

Soccer camp is fun! Coach says I did something great in today's game— I scored the winning goal. Alex almost stole the ball from me, but I ran faster. Coach began to shout from the side of the field. It felt like a scene from a movie. Now I need to wash the dirt off my uniform so I can wear it again tomorrow. I'll write more later!

Love,

Jada

Stop and Check

Circle your best word.

Compare and Contrast

Draw and identify two types of animals.

Animal 1

Animal 2

Write about how these animals are alike and how they are different. Be sure to include facts and details about each animal. Remember to indent the first line of each paragraph you write and leave space for margins.

Fiction or Nonfiction?

Which type of text do you like to read better: fiction (imagined) or nonfiction (real)? Write your opinion, reasons to support your opinion, and a concluding statement. Remember to indent the first line of each paragraph you write and leave space for margins.

Last Weekend

Write about what you did last weekend. Be sure to include temporal words (such as *first, next, then, later, finally*) to show the order of events. Remember to indent the first line of each paragraph you write and leave space for margins.

How To

Explain how to complete a favorite activity or make a special food. List each step in order. Use linking words (such as *and, but, or*) to connect ideas. Remember to indent the first line of each paragraph you write and leave space for margins.

Handwriting and the Writing Process

Write a Paragraph

A paragraph is a group of sentences about one subject.
Write a paragraph about your school.

I. Prewriting

Prewriting means gathering ideas and planning before you write.
List your ideas on a piece of paper. Then plan your paragraph, telling
the subject and in what order you will write your ideas.

2. Drafting

Drafting means putting your thoughts into written sentences for the
first time. Use the ideas you listed in Prewriting to draft your paragraph.
Write your first draft.

3. Revising

Revising means changing your writing to make it say exactly what
you mean. Read your draft. Mark any changes you want to make.

Does your writing include all the information readers want to know?   Yes   No

4. Editing

Editing means checking your revised writing for errors in spelling,
punctuation, capitalization, and handwriting.

Are all words spelled correctly?	Yes	No
Have you used uppercase letters and punctuation correctly?	Yes	No
Do your letters have good shape and size?	Yes	No
Does your writing have good spacing?	Yes	No
Does your writing have good slant?	Yes	No
Is your writing easy to read?	Yes	No

5. Publishing

Publishing means using your best handwriting to make a good
copy of your writing. Share your writing with others.

Writing Quickly

Writing quickly is a skill that will help when you need to write a story, take a timed test, or take notes.

Writing that is done quickly should still be easy to read. With practice, you will learn how to write quickly and still have legible handwriting.

Read the saying. Write it quickly and legibly.

Handwriting Tutor

In fourteen hundred ninety-two Columbus sailed the ocean blue.

Now write the lines again.
Try to write them faster this time.

Write the saying two more times.
Try to write it even faster, but keep it easy to read.

Now read your final writing. Circle Yes or No to respond to each statement. Then show your writing to another reader, either a classmate or your teacher. Ask that person to circle Yes or No beside each statement.

	My Evaluation		My Classmate's or Teacher's Evaluation	
The writing is easy to read.	Yes	No	Yes	No
The writing has good Shape.	Yes	No	Yes	No
The writing has good Size.	Yes	No	Yes	No
The writing has good Spacing.	Yes	No	Yes	No
The writing has good Slant.	Yes	No	Yes	No

Writing Easily

As you write stories and essays for school papers and tests, it is important that your handwriting flows easily. When you automatically know how to write legibly, you don't have to worry about your handwriting. You are free to think about what you want your writing to say. With practice, you will learn how to make your writing easy, quick, and legible.

Read the writing prompt below. Respond to it by writing on the lines. Let your handwriting flow easily as you think and write.

> Think about a time when you were surprised by someone or something.
>
> Write a story about what happened when you were surprised. Include details to make your writing interesting.

Now read your writing. Circle Yes or No to respond to each statement. Then show your writing to another reader, either a classmate or your teacher. Ask that person to circle Yes or No beside each statement.

	My Evaluation		My Classmate's or Teacher's Evaluation	
The writing is easy to read.	Yes	No	Yes	No
The writing has good Shape.	Yes	No	Yes	No
The writing has good Size.	Yes	No	Yes	No
The writing has good Spacing.	Yes	No	Yes	No
The writing has good Slant.	Yes	No	Yes	No

I'd Like To Be a Lighthouse

I'd like to be a lighthouse
    And scrubbed and painted white.
I'd like to be a lighthouse
    And stay awake all night
To keep my eye on everything
    That sails my patch of sea;
I'd like to be a lighthouse
    With the ships all watching me.

Rachel Field

Write the poem in your best cursive handwriting. Be sure to leave space for margins.

Write the Sentence

The quick brown fox jumps over the lazy dog.

The quick brown fox jumps over the lazy dog.

Record of Student's Handwriting Skills
Cursive

	Needs Improvement	Shows Mastery		Needs Improvement	Shows Mastery
Sits correctly	❑	❑	Writes the undercurve-to-undercurve joining	❑	❑
Positions paper correctly	❑	❑	Writes the undercurve-to-downcurve joining	❑	❑
Holds pencil correctly	❑	❑	Writes the undercurve-to-overcurve joining	❑	❑
Writes undercurve strokes	❑	❑	Writes the checkstroke-to-undercurve joining	❑	❑
Writes downcurve strokes	❑	❑	Writes the checkstroke-to-downcurve joining	❑	❑
Writes overcurve strokes	❑	❑	Writes the checkstroke-to-overcurve joining	❑	❑
Writes slant strokes	❑	❑	Writes the overcurve-to-undercurve joining	❑	❑
Writes *i, t, u, w*	❑	❑	Writes the overcurve-to-downcurve joining	❑	❑
Writes *e, l, b, h, f, k*	❑	❑	Writes the overcurve-to-overcurve joining	❑	❑
Writes *r, s, j, p*	❑	❑	Writes with correct shape	❑	❑
Writes *a, d, g, o, c, q*	❑	❑	Writes with correct size	❑	❑
Writes *n, m, y, x, v, z*	❑	❑	Writes with correct spacing	❑	❑
Writes numerals *1–10*	❑	❑	Writes with correct slant	❑	❑
Writes *A, O, D, C, E*	❑	❑	Regularly checks written work for legibility	❑	❑
Writes *N, M, H, K*	❑	❑			
Writes *U, Y, Z*	❑	❑			
Writes *V, W, X*	❑	❑			
Writes *I, J, Q*	❑	❑			
Writes *T, F*	❑	❑			
Writes *G, S, L*	❑	❑			
Writes *P, R, B*	❑	❑			

Index